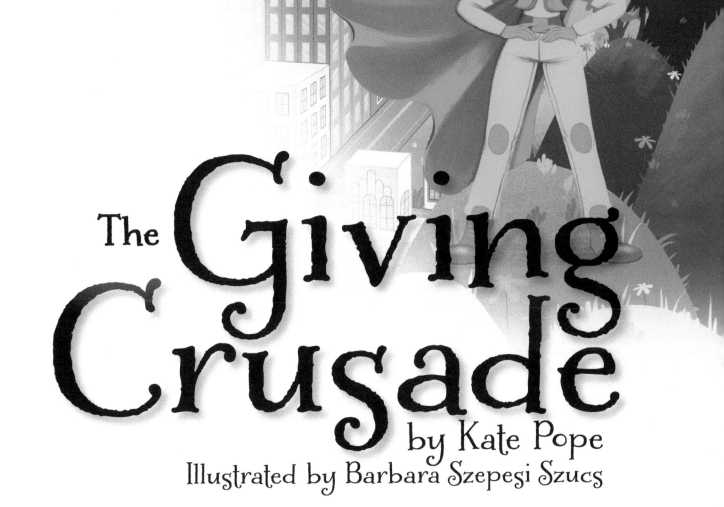

The Giving Crusade

by Kate Pope

Illustrated by Barbara Szepesi Szucs

ISBN: 978-0-9894814-0-3

Edited by Amy Ashby

Published by Warren Publishing
Charlotte, NC
www.warrenpublishing.net
Printed in the United States

For my niece, Annie.
May you live joyfully, grow
gracefully, and give generously.
With my love, always.

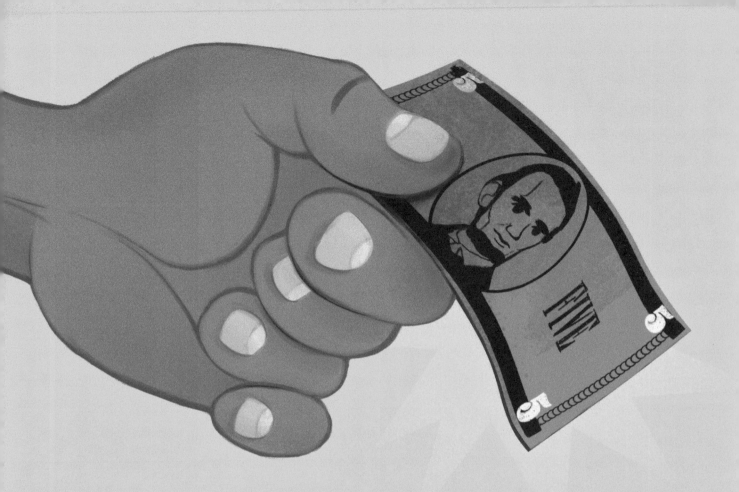

Hi there, my friend!
I have five bucks for you.
But this gift comes with rules,
here's what you must do:

Give it away!

This money's not meant to go to a friend,
but should be given in a way so you don't see it again.

Talk with your parents, your teachers, and friends to figure out how and where you'll begin.

You might give it to kids who don't feel so swell; or send it abroad to help build a well;

maybe buy a meal to feed children in need;
or buy a book for a school so kids can read.

Simply find something in which you believe
and give away every bit of this green.

Search your community and also your school,
and you'll learn this world's much bigger than you.

It doesn't matter that the amount is small,
just find a way to get rid of it all.

Or, better yet, you can make this cash grow,
by including a few of the people you know.

When this money's all spent, don't let your effort stop there,

roll up your sleeves to show folks you care.

Volunteer at a shelter or on a hospital wing,
where making a difference won't cost you a thing.

Give your time and your gifts to the things you believe,
and you will always have more than you need.

Live your life with a little compassion and grace,
and watch as this world becomes a much better place.

CPSIA information can be obtained
at www.ICGtesting.com
Printed in the USA
LVHW01*0533310818
588585LV00005B/8/P